THE WORLD OF
FLASHPOINT

FEATURING

THE WORLD OF

FLASHPOINT

FEATURING
GREEN LANTERN

ABIN SUR: THE GREEN LANTERN
ADAM SCHLAGMAN writer
FELIPE MASSAFERA ROBSON ROCHA JOE PRADO artists
ROD REIS colorist
DAVE SHARPE letterer

SPECIAL THANKS TO GEOFF JOHNS

FRANKENSTEIN AND THE CREATURES OF THE UNKNOWN
JEFF LEMIRE writer
IBRAIM ROBERSON ALEX MASSACCI
ANDY SMITH KEITH CHAMPAGNE artists
PETE PANTAZIS colorist
PAT BROSSEAU TRAVIS LANHAM letterers

GREEN ARROW INDUSTRIES
PORNSAK PICHETSHOTE writer
IG GUARA MARCO CASTIELLO RUY JOSÉ VINCENZO ACUNZO artists
STEFANI RENNEE colorist
CARLOS M. MANGUAL letterer

HAL JORDAN
ADAM SCHLAGMAN writer
CLIFF RICHARDS BEN OLIVER artists
ALLEN PASSALAQUA colorist
WES ABBOTT letterer

Collection Cover by Felipe Massafera

Barry Allen awoke in a world he barely recognizes, but it isn't a trick or a parallel Earth. Something or someone has altered time, replacing Barry's world with this one. And this new world is not a safe place.

The planet is on the brink of destruction as Wonder Woman and the Amazons wage war with Aquaman and the Atlanteans without any regard for the powerless masses caught in the middle. As a result, most of Europe is either destroyed or occupied territory, and the rest of the world lives in constant fear. A few motley heroes are mounting a resistance, but in this world heroes are hard to come by. No one has ever heard of the Flash, or the Justice League, or Superman. Hal Jordan was never given a Green Lantern ring, and Bruce Wayne was killed in Crime Alley when he was just a little boy.

Without his powers or his friends to aid him, Barry reaches out to a new Batman, Bruce's father Thomas Wayne, who survived in this reality while his son did not. Now they are working together to put the world right. If they fail, they'll never escape from this twisted, tragic world.

Welcome to...

BRIAN CUNNINGHAM
JOEY CAVALIERI
Editors – Original Series

DARREN SHAN
KATE STEWART
Assistant Editors – Original Series

IAN SATTLER
Director – Editorial, Special Projects and Archival Editions

ROBIN WILDMAN
Editor

ROBBIN BROSTERMAN
Design Director – Books

ROBBIE BIEDERMAN
Publication Design

EDDIE BERGANZA
Executive Editor

BOB HARRAS
VP – Editor-in-Chief

DIANE NELSON
President

DAN DIDIO and JIM LEE
Co-Publishers

GEOFF JOHNS
Chief Creative Officer

JOHN ROOD
Executive VP – Sales, Marketing and Business Development

AMY GENKINS
Senior VP – Business and Legal Affairs

NAIRI GARDINER
Senior VP – Finance

JEFF BOISON
VP – Publishing Operations

MARK CHIARELLO
VP – Art Direction and Design

JOHN CUNNINGHAM
VP – Marketing

TERRI CUNNINGHAM
VP – Talent Relations and Services

ALISON GILL
Senior VP – Manufacturing and Operations

DAVID HYDE
VP – Publicity

HANK KANALZ
Senior VP – Digital

JAY KOGAN
VP – Business and Legal Affairs, Publishing

JACK MAHAN
VP – Business Affairs, Talent

NICK NAPOLITANO
VP – Manufacturing Administration

SUE POHJA
VP – Book Sales

COURTNEY SIMMONS
Senior VP – Publicity

BOB WAYNE
Senior VP – Sales

FLASHPOINT: THE WORLD OF FLASHPOINT FEATURING GREEN LANTERN Published by DC Comics. Cover and compilation Copyright © 2012 DC Comics. All Rights Reserved. Originally published in single magazine form in FLASHPOINT: ABIN SUR—THE GREEN LANTERN 1-3, FLASHPOINT: FRANKENSTEIN AND THE CREATURES OF THE UNKNOWN 1-3, FLASHPOINT: GREEN ARROW INDUSTRIES 1, FLASHPOINT: HAL JORDAN 1-3 Copyright © 2011 DC Comics. All Rights Reserved. All characters, their distinctive likenesses and related elements featured in this publication are trademarks of DC Comics. The stories, characters and incidents featured in this publication are entirely fictional. DC Comics does not read or accept unsolicited ideas, stories or artwork.

DC Comics, 1700 Broadway, New York, NY 10019
A Warner Bros. Entertainment Company.
Printed by RR Donnelley, Salem, VA, USA. 2/17/12. First Printing.
ISBN: 978-1-4012-3406-5

SUSTAINABLE
FORESTRY
INITIATIVE

Certified Chain of Custody
At Least 25% Certified Forest Content

www.sfiprogram.org
SFI-01042
APPLIES TO TEXT STOCK ONLY

ABIN SUR
THE GREEN LANTERN

ADAM SCHLAGMAN
Writer

PART ONE: EMERALD ISOLATION
Art by **FELIPE MASSAFERA**

PART TWO: EMERALD CONNECTION
Art by **ROBSON ROCHA, FELIPE MASSAFERA** & **JOE PRADO**

PART THREE: EMERALD EMBRACE
Art by **ROBSON ROCHA** & **FELIPE MASSAFERA**

Covers by **FELIPE MASSAFERA**

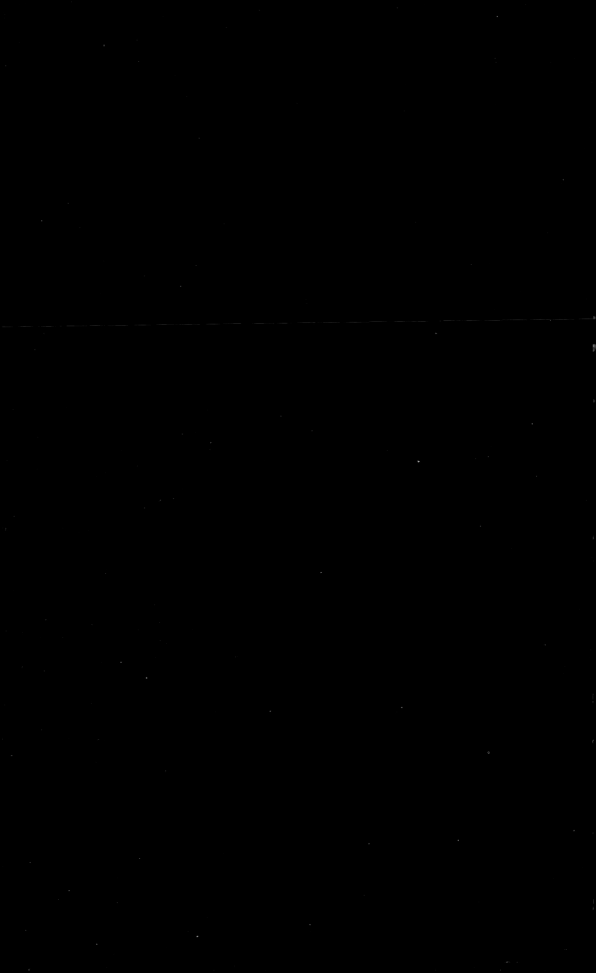

LANTERN 2814!

WHAT IS YOUR STATUS? WHERE IS THE WHITE ENTITY?

I WILL RETRIEVE THE ENTITY AS SOON AS EARTH IS SAFE.

NO. EARTH IS ALREADY LOST.

IF YOU DO NOT RETRIEVE THE ENTITY AT ONCE...

...YOU WILL BE STRIPPED OF YOUR RING.

ABIN!

ABIN?!

NO. THE GUARDIANS DO NOT KNOW I AM HERE.

I NEED TO TELL YOU OF A *PROPHECY* FORETOLD BY *ATROCITUS*.

PROPHECY?

"HE CALLED IT THE *FLASHPOINT*."

WHAT MADNESS DO YOU SPEAK OF?

A FLASHPOINT IS A MOMENT IN TIME THAT CHANGES EVERYTHING MOVING FORWARD.

SOMEONE FROM EARTH ALTERED HISTORY...AND NOT JUST OF THIS WORLD...BUT THE ENTIRE UNIVERSE.

NO, ABIN. YOU ARE MISTAKEN.

I DO NOT UNDERSTAND.

B-BUT IF YOU ARE HERE...

...THEN... THEN I HAVE FAILED.

YOU HAVE DONE A TREMENDOUS JOB PROTECTING LIFE...

...BUT YOU HAVE NOT LET YOURSELF EXPERIENCE IT.

YOU CANNOT JUST SOAR ABOVE, BUT MUST REMAIN IN TOUCH WITH ALL THINGS.

REMEMBER, ABIN, WE ARE ALL CONNECTED.

SO EMBRACE YOUR DESTINY...

ABIN SUR OF UNGARA.

FRANKENSTEIN AND THE
CREATURES OF THE UNKNOWN

JEFF LEMIRE
Writer

PART ONE: WEIRD WAR TALES
Art by **IBRAIM ROBERSON**
Cover by **DOUG MAHNKE** with **ROD REIS**

PART TWO: OUR ARMY AT GORE
Art by **IBRAIM ROBERSON** & **ALEX MASSACCI**
Cover by **DOUG MAHNKE** with **CHRISTIAN ALAMY**

PART THREE: OUR FRIGHTENING FORCES
Pencils by **ANDY SMITH**
Inks by **KEITH CHAMPAGNE**
Cover by **DOUG MAHNKE** with **ROD REIS**

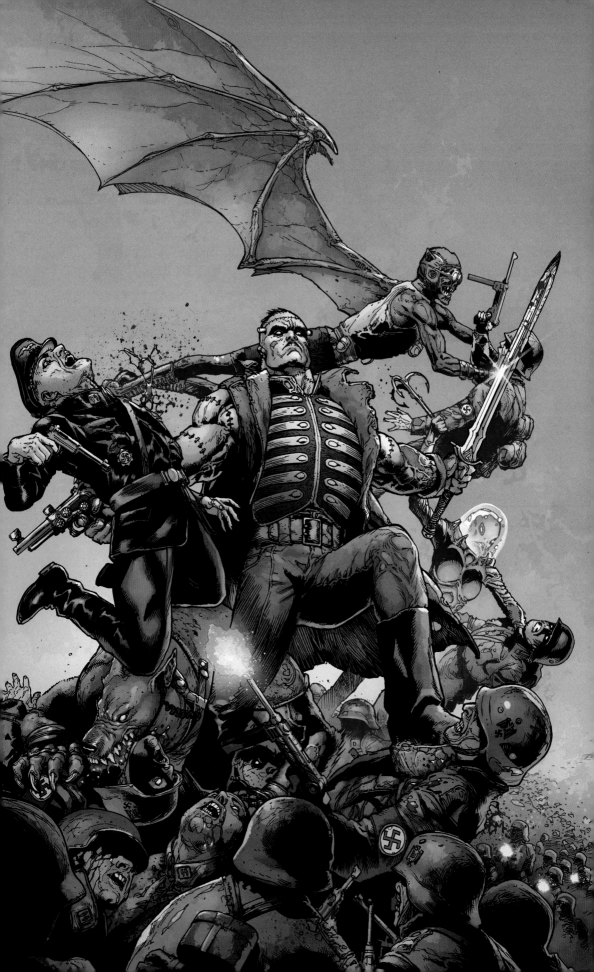

1942. The North Atlantic.

DAY SIX IN THIS FROZEN *HELL* AND STILL NO SIGN OF JERRY.*

*THE GERMANS. --ED.

ABOUT TEN DAYS AGO, WE RECEIVED REPORTS OF A NAZI PATROL UNIT IN THE AREA SENDING INFO ABOUT OUR SUBMARINE LOCATIONS BACK TO GERMANY.

I DON'T KNOW WHERE WE GOT OUR INTEL...BUT I'M STARTING TO THINK THERE'S *NOTHING* UP HERE EXCEPT ICE.

MY MEN ARE COLD AND MISERABLE AND I'M ABOUT READY TO CALL THIS ENTIRE OPERATION OFF--

EH?

SIR? I THINK... I THINK THERE'S... *SOMETHING* OVER HERE.

WHAT IN *HELL*--?!

LT. SHRIEVE, SIR...WHAT IN THE *NAME OF GOD* IS THAT THING!?

I DON'T--

HODGE!

BLAM!

UNG--!

WAS...

...SOMETHING...

...LEFT...

...UNDONE?

IT WAS THE HANDIWORK OF THE MODERN PROMETHEUS, VICTOR FRANKENSTEIN...HIS PATCHWORK MAN. I HAD READ ABOUT HIM, BUT TO *SEE* HIM, THERE *ALIVE*...AND WHOSE SIDE WOULD HE BE ON?

AHHHH...I HEAR RADIO...RADAR...THIS BRAVE NEW WORLD...THIS DISTANT CENTURY.

AND STILL THERE'S SO MUCH...EVIL.

WOULD HE BE ONE *MORE* MONSTER AMONG SO MANY OTHERS?

SCHLUNKU

AND WHERE EVIL WALKS... FRANKENSTEIN LIVES!

THE TIME FOR TALKING IS OVER.

MEIN GOTT!

ABWEICHUNG!

BLAM! BLAM! BLAM!

YOU ARE RIGHT... EVIL THING. MY FLESH MAY INDEED BE A TWISTED ABERRATION...

BUT INSIDE LIVES THE SOUL OF A MAN. THE SAME CANNOT BE SAID FOR YOU!

SHLUNK!

MEET THE PRIDE AND JOY OF THE *G.I. ROBOT PROGRAM...* J.A.K.E., THE JOINT ACTION KILLING ENGINE!

YOU WILL STAND DOWN OR BE TAKEN BY FORCE.

URK! THERE...IS...NO LIFE INSIDE OF THIS...THIS THING.

I DO NOT FEAR YOU, METAL MAN. IT IS YOU WHO WILL STAND DOWN!

FEAR IS IRRELEVANT. YOU ARE OBSOLETE. YOU ARE TO BE DECOMMISSIONED IMMEDIATELY.

BY ANY MEANS NECESSARY.

SHUT THAT DAMN THING OFF, CRANE!

CLANK! CLANK! CLANK!

YOU WILL NOT BE ALLOWED TO INTERFERE, LT. SHRIEVE.

FWP! FWP!

UNG!

THIS MACHINE CANNOT KILL ME. NOTHING CAN.

KILL YOU? YOU REALLY THINK WHAT YOU HAVE IS "LIFE"? YOU'RE UNNATURAL... *UNHOLY.*

AND YOU DESERVE TO BE PUT DOWN LIKE THE *HORROR SHOW* THAT YOU ARE.

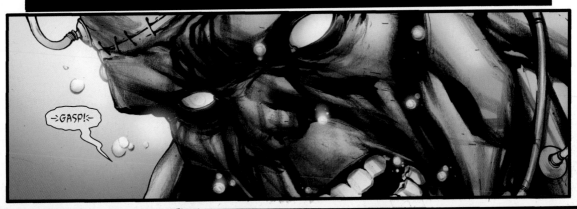

WHA?!

GRRRR.

FRANKENSTEIN? WH-WHERE ARE WE?

EASY, GIRL... EASY.

RRRR... SNIFF SNIFF!

OH GOD...I THOUGHT YOU WERE ALL JUST PART OF SOME HORRIBLY *DULL* DREAM.

SAVE IT, BLOODSUCKER... WE NEED TO MOVE.

WHERE... AM WE... GO?

JUST STAY CLOSE TO ME, GRIFFITH. WE'LL BE OKAY.

THIS PLACE IS FILLED WITH DARKNESS. FOLLOW ME AND BE READY FOR ANYTHING.

÷SIGH÷... WHO *DIED* AND MADE *HIM* LEADER...?

I THINK WE *ALL* DID.

RELAX, PRINCESS; YOU'RE NOT MY TYPE...

I PREFER MY MEALS WARM-BLOODED.

GRRRRRP

ENOUGH, LEECH!

ALL OF YOU... WE ARE RUNNING OUT OF TIME. THIS BICKERING IS USELESS. WE CAN'T AFFORD TO STAY HERE. THEY WILL COME AFTER US.

AND JUST WHERE THE HELL ARE WE SUPPOSED TO GO?!

GOTHAM. MY FATHER HAD A SECRET LAB THERE. WE LIVED THERE WHEN I WAS VERY YOUNG...A PLACE CALLED SLAUGHTER SWAMP.

BUT MAZURSKY WOULD BE OVER A HUNDRED YEARS OLD NOW.

YES, BUT HIS WORK, HIS NOTES, THEY MIGHT STILL BE INTACT.

THEN GOTHAM IT IS. IF WE HAVE ANY CHANCE OF CHANGING YOU BACK, IT IS IN THIS...SLAUGHTER SWAMP.

SOUNDS POSITIVELY CHARMING.

TRUTH IS...WE'D ALL BUT FORGOTTEN THEY WERE EVEN STILL DOWN HERE, SIR...I HAVE NO IDEA HOW THEY GOT OUT!

IT DOESN'T MATTER NOW, DOES IT? *THEY'RE GONE.*

WHA--WHAT SHOULD I DO, GENERAL LANE?

WHAT SHOULD *YOU* DO?

NOTHING, YOU SNIVELING LITTLE WORM... THESE ARE *MONSTERS* WE'RE TALKING ABOUT.

"NOT SOME STUPID, JACKED-UP LAB RATS...BONA FIDE, HONEST-TO-GOD *MONSTERS.*

"AND WHEN-EVER THERE ARE MONSTERS THAT NEED KILLING, I ALWAYS KNOW WHAT TO DO...

SPLASH!

SPLOOSH!

SCHLINK!

"I CALL THE ONE PERSON BORN TO *KILL* MONSTERS...

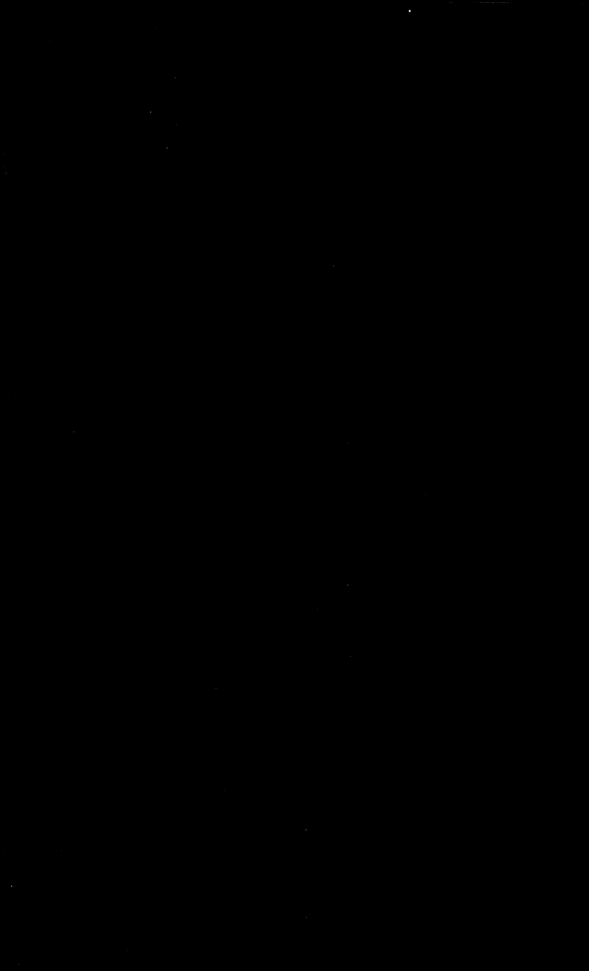

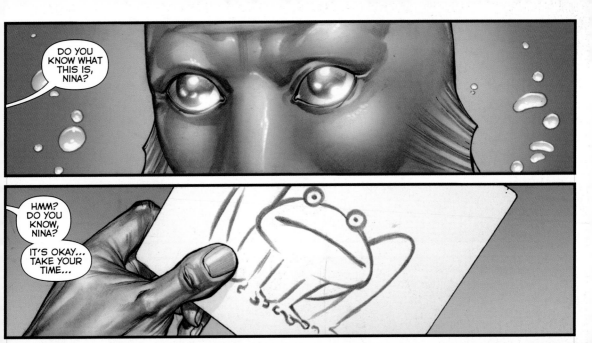

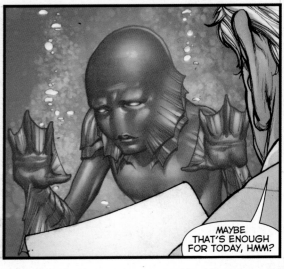

THIS THING'S BEEN IN MOTHBALLS FOR DECADES! ARE YOU SURE IT WILL EVEN STILL WORK, CRANE?

I BUILD THINGS TO LAST, LANE! HE'LL WORK ALL RIGHT. J.A.K.E. HAS JUST BEEN WAITING FOR THIS OPPORTUNITY...

THERE! SEE, HE'S READY.

KZZT-- HELLO, DR. CRANE. IT IS GOOD TO SEE YOU AGAIN.

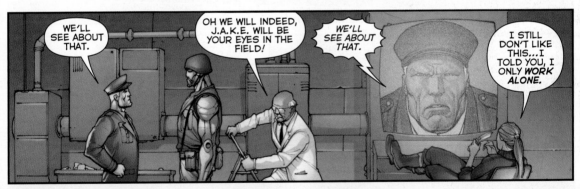

WE'LL SEE ABOUT THAT.

OH WE WILL INDEED, J.A.K.E. WILL BE YOUR EYES IN THE FIELD!

WE'LL SEE ABOUT THAT.

I STILL DON'T LIKE THIS...I TOLD YOU, I ONLY WORK ALONE.

YOU WORK WITH WHOEVER I SAY YOU WORK WITH, JUNIOR.

AND WHAT IF I DON'T... YOU GOT ANOTHER KICK-ASS BLACK-OPS MONSTER HUNTER ON CALL THAT I DON'T KNOW ABOUT?

G.I. ROBOT MAY BE OLD, BUT HE STILL HAS A FEW SPECIAL SKILLS THAT MAY PROVE PARTICULARLY USEFUL AGAINST ONE OF THE TARGETS.

BESIDES...ONCE I TELL YOU WHO THE TARGETS ARE, YOU'LL DO WHATEVER I SAY FOR A CRACK AT THEM...TRUST ME.

UH-HUH, SURE. WHY DON'T YOU ENLIGHTEN ME THEN, "BOSS." BUT BEFORE YOU DO, THERE'S JUST ONE THING...

AND WHAT'S THAT?

YOU CALL ME "JUNIOR" AGAIN AND I TAKE YOUR EYE.

I DON'T DOUBT YOU WOULD. BUT WHY DON'T YOU SAVE THAT ENERGY FOR THE MISSION...YOU'LL NEED IT.

IT'S THEM, SHRIEVE... THE GREAT "CREATURE COMMANDOS"...

NOW SHARPEN YOUR STAKES AND POLISH YOUR CROSSES, OR WHATEVER IT IS YOU NEED TO DO TO GET READY...

WE JUST PICKED UP THE TRACERS THEY PUT IN THEM BACK IN '45...THEY'RE IN GOTHAM. TIME TO MOVE.

IT LOOKS AS THOUGH YOUR FATHER LEFT VERY LITTLE BEHIND.

SNIFF... SNIFF...

I...THERE WAS MORE... I WAS ONLY THREE OR FOUR...I DON'T *REALLY* REMEMBER MUCH...BUT I DO REMEMBER A FULL LABORATORY HERE.

SNIFF! SNIFF!

HERE... DOWN.

HRMM...

CRACK!

HMM...IT SEEMS THE CABIN IS OVER A SEPARATE POCKET OF WATER.

KREENCH!

HIS LAB!

IT SEEMS YOUR FATHER WAS A MAN OF MANY SECRETS.

NO ONE HAS BEEN HERE FOR QUITE SOME TIME, I'D SAY.

OH, FRANK...I REMEMBER IT SO WELL...THIS IS WHERE I SPENT MY CHILDHOOD...DOWN HERE, NOT IN THAT OLD CABIN.

MY GOD, HOW DID HE BUILD THIS PLACE?

I DON'T UNDERSTAND. YOU SAID YOU MADE ME LIKE THIS BECAUSE I WAS SO SICK AS A LITTLE GIRL. YOU SAID CHANGING ME WAS THE ONLY WAY TO KEEP ME ALIVE...

BUT THESE CREATURES... I WAS *ONE OF THEM*, WASN'T I?...I WAS NEVER A NORMAL GIRL. YOU *TOOK ME* FROM THIS PLACE.

I WAS SO LONELY AND YOU WERE THE TINIEST, MOST BEAUTIFUL THING I'D EVER SEEN... I'M SO SORRY...

HURK!!

GRIFFITH!?

WHAT DID THEY DO TO HIM?

IT WAS A SILVER BULLET.

SILVER!?

HURRY, GET HIM INTO THE CASTLE...WE HAVEN'T MUCH TIME!

...RIP THE METAL BRAINS RIGHT OUT OF YOUR IDEAPOT!

THOOM

KZZT

KZZT

THWACK

FRANKENSTEIN ELECTRICAL DISCHARGE WEAPON.

CLICK-CLICK-CLICK

DAMMIT!

I'VE REMOVED THE BULLET AND STOPPED THE BLEEDING, BUT THE SILVER POISONING IS IRREVERSIBLE IN THE LUPENS...

HOWEVER, IF I REVERSE THE PROCEDURE THAT TURNED HIM INTO A WEREWOLF IN THE FIRST PLACE...TURN HIM BACK INTO A MAN... HE'LL BE IMMUNE TO THE SILVER.

CAN YOU DO THAT?

OF COURSE. I MAY HAVE LIED ABOUT MANY THINGS...BUT NOT THAT. I PROMISED VELCORO AND GRIFFITH THEY'D BE MEN AGAIN...

HURRN...

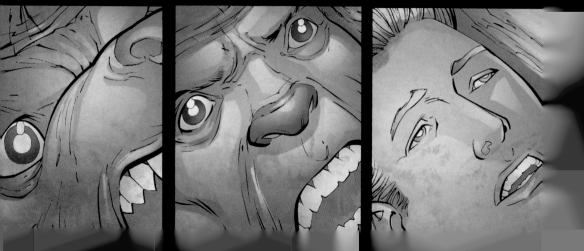

FRANKENSTEIN AND THE CREATURES OF THE UNKNOWN

PART 3: OUR FRIGHTENING FORCES

GREEN ARROW
INDUSTRIES

PORNSAK PICHETSHOTE
Writer

IG GUARA
MARCO CASTIELLO
Pencillers

RUY JOSÉ
VINCENZO ACUNZO
Inkers

Cover by **VIKTOR KALVACHEV**

"WE WANTED *GREEN ARROW* TO BE DIFFERENT."

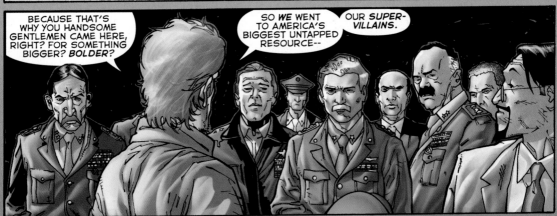

BECAUSE THAT'S WHY YOU HANDSOME GENTLEMEN CAME HERE, RIGHT? FOR SOMETHING BIGGER? *BOLDER?*

SO *WE* WENT TO AMERICA'S BIGGEST UNTAPPED RESOURCE--

OUR *SUPER-VILLAINS.*

"SEE, THE *TRICKSTER*-- WE JUST CAUGHT HIM AND HIS ANTIGRAVITY BOOTS.

"*HE* USES THEM TO RUN ON AIR, BUT YOU KNOW WHAT? ADD ROCKET PROPULSION TO THAT TECH, AND YOU GET SUPER-SPEED FLIGHT.

"*THE FOLDED MAN'S SUIT* LETS HIM ACCESS 2D- AND 4D-SPACE...

"WHICH MEANS *WE* CAN USE IT TO SHRINK LARGE WEAPONRY INTO PORTABLE SIZES.

"THEN THERE'S THE *TOP*. HIS ARSENAL OF SUPER-POWERED TOPS INCLUDES AN ATOMIC GRENADE TOP WITH THE POWER OF FIVE NUKES.

"AND LET ME JUST SAY THOSE WORDS AGAIN, 'CUZ WHO KNOWS THE NEXT CHANCE I'LL GET TO: AN *ATOMIC GRENADE TOP*, PEOPLE."

OKAY, *COMBINE* THAT STUFF. WHAT DO YOU GET? *ONE:* THE CONCLUSION THAT WE COMPLAIN ABOUT PUBLIC SCHOOL EDUCATION TOO MUCH, APPARENTLY.

TWO: SOMETHING *NEW.* SOMETHING TO *REALLY* MAKE THE BAD GUYS SWEAT.

GENTLEMEN, AND... UH, *MORE* GENTLEMEN, I PRESENT TO YOU--

YOU BROUGHT A *BOW* JUST SO YOU CAN POSE WITH YOUR MISSILES?

HEY, THEY *LAUGHED*, DIDN'T THEY? AND IF THERE'S ONE THING THOSE GENERALS NEED TO BE, IT'S *HAPPY* WITH US. WHERE ARE THEY, BY THE WAY?

DOWNSTAIRS. AND SINCE WHEN DO WE *ENTERTAIN* HERE? THIS ISLAND'S FOR--

"THE ISLAND'S FOR TOP-SECRET WEAPONS TESTING." I KNOW. I *BOUGHT* THE PLACE, REMEMBER? WHY ARE YOU SO UPTIGHT LATE--

BA-DOOP

EUROPEAN PEAC
TALKS FAIL

As stakes between Themyscirans and Atlanteans escalate, more and more Americans worry the the war might affect their liv

SEE? YOUR E-READER'S WHY I'M SO UPTIGHT LATELY.

PEOPLE ARE FREAKED OUT ENOUGH RIGHT NOW.

LISTEN... A WHILE BACK, MY RIGHT-HAND MAN STOLE A *FORTUNE* FROM ME. AND I MEAN *FORTUNE*. I NEVER SAW HIM AGAIN.

BUT IT LEFT QUEEN INDUSTRIES A WEAPONS MANUFACTURER WITH NO MONEY FOR R&D.

SO I SPENT WHAT LITTLE I HAD AND HIRED AN *EX-MILITARY TEAM*. FIGURE SUPER-VILLAIN-HEAT-GUN-*THIS*, FREEZE-BEAM-*THAT*, WHY NOT JUST *CAPTURE* THEM AND *REPACKAGE* THEIR WEAPONS FOR THE GOVERNMENT?

BECAUSE THE SHORTEST DISTANCE BETWEEN TWO POINTS IS A STRAIGHT LINE, AND IN THE RIGHT HANDS, *MONEY* IS A GREEN ARROW TO THE FUTURE.

THAT'S WHAT *GREEN ARROW INDUSTRIES* IS ABOUT.

IT'S ABOUT NOT BEING AFRAID OF CHANGE.

SAYS THE MAN WITH EIGHT DIFFERENT KIDS FROM SEVEN DIFFERENT WOMEN.

HEY, I MARRIED *SOME* OF THEM.

YEAH. SUPERMODELS, MOVIE STARS...IS THERE ANYONE YOU *HAVEN'T* SLEPT WITH?

OLLIE, LISTEN-- FOR THE FIRST TIME IN A LONG TIME, AMERICA DOESN'T FEEL LIKE THE SUPER POWER IT USED TO BE.

OUR ARMIES AREN'T THE *TOUGHEST* ANYMORE. OUR ECONOMY'S NOT THE *STRONGEST*. BUT VIOLENCE AROUND THE WORLD IS STILL DRAGGING US IN.

YEAH, AND WEAPONS MANUFACTURE IS BRINGING MORE JOBS TO OUR ECONOMY THAN ANY OTHER SECTOR RIGHT NOW.

GOD, WHY IS BIG BUSINESS *AUTOMATICALLY* THE BAD GUY?

SO WHY NOT *MAKE* IT THE *GOOD* GUY? WE HAVE SUPERHERO SOLDIERS, ALIENS, ROBOTS, PETS...

...WHAT WOULD IT TAKE TO MAKE A *CORPORATION* A SUPERHERO?

ROY, SERIOUSLY--

SERIOUSLY. WHAT WOULD IT LOOK LIKE? A COMPANY THAT FOUGHT FOR PEOPLE AND INSPIRED THEM? ONE THEY *TRUSTED*?

IDENTITY VERIFIED:

ROY HARPER

YOU'RE THE ONE ALWAYS EMPHASIZING THINKING BIGGER.

WELL, I'VE BEEN YOUR CHIEF OF SECURITY FOR FIVE YEARS. I *KNOW* YOU. YOU'RE *MORE* THAN SOME GUY WHO MAKES MISSILES. MARK MY WORDS--

--YOU HAVE IT IN YOU TO DO SOMETHING INSPIRING, OLLIE, AND I'M GOING TO WATCH YOU DO IT.

DEAD.

COME ON, COME ON...

WHAT THE HELL JUST...

MY GUYS, *THEIR* GUYS--

IF IT WASN'T FOR *ROY*, I'D BE--

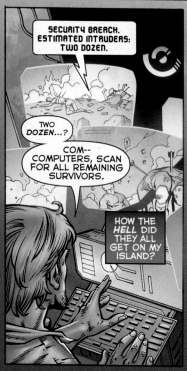

SECURITY BREACH. ESTIMATED INTRUDERS: TWO DOZEN.

TWO DOZEN...?

COM-- COMPUTERS, SCAN FOR ALL REMAINING SURVIVORS.

HOW THE *HELL* DID THEY ALL GET ON MY ISLAND?

SURVIVORS: ONE. ESCAPING VICINITY.

FEMALE RAIDER?

WHAT? *EVERYONE* ELSE...?

OH GOD, THE *GENERALS*...

ACCORDING TO THIS, THE--THE RAIDERS WERE ORGANIZED. THEY SMUGGLED CHEMICAL BOMBS, LONGBOWS AND ARROWS THROUGH OUR SECURITY SCREENS...

...AND I HAVE NO IDEA *WHY*.

SURVIVORS: ONE. ESCAPING VICINITY.

"YOU HAVE IT IN YOU TO DO SOMETHING INSPIRING, OLLIE, AND I'M GOING TO WATCH YOU DO IT.

"YOU HAVE IT IN YOU TO DO SOMETHING..."

:KAFF:

YOU...ARE LUCKIER THAN ANYONE HAS THE RIGHT... TO BE...

YOUR STORY FROM BEFORE. FINISH IT.

HOW DID YOU GET THROUGH OUR SECURITY? HOW DO YOU KNOW SO MUCH ABOUT US?

...DO YOU HAVE ANY IDEA HOW MANY OF YOUR *OWN* SECURITY TEAM COME FROM TOWNS YOU'VE RUINED?

THEY *FED* US INFORMATION.

AND WHEN WE HEARD THE GENERALS WERE COMING...WE KNEW *THEIR* DEATHS HERE WOULD START MEDIA INQUIRIES, AND UNDER *THAT* MICROSCOPE?

EVERYTHING GREEN ARROW INDUSTRIES IS HIDING--ALL THE *PEOPLE* IT'S ENDANGERING... PEOPLE WILL *KNOW.*

I--I SWEAR TO GOD, I DIDN'T KNOW HOW BAD IT GOT IN THOSE TOWNS.

I...HAVE PEOPLE WHO DEAL WITH THAT STUFF.

PLEASE. IT WOULDN'T HAVE CHANGED ANYTHING IF YOU DID. YOU'D BE TOO BUSY THINKING ABOUT YOUR BOTTOM LINE.

NO!

...SEEMS LIKE SHE *DID* HAVE SUPER-POWERS, SIR. ENHANCED SPEED AND AGILITY. THAT'S HOW SHE SURVIVED WHEN ALL HER TEAMMATES DIED.

WE THINK IT WAS FROM THAT AMULET AROUND HER NECK. IF IT IS, WE'LL PUT IT THROUGH THE SYSTEM LIKE EVERYTHING ELSE.

WHAT?

WEAPONIZE IT. YOU KNOW. LIKE WE ALWAYS DO.

GOD, I'D LOVE TO KNOW WHERE A KID LIKE THAT GOT A SUPER-POWERED *AMULET.*

SHE...*STOLE* IT FROM HER MOTHER. A SUPER-VILLAIN NAMED VIXEN...

SIR? YOU *KNOW* WHO THAT GIRL IS?

NO...I--

GOD, I HAVE NO *IDEA* WHO SHE IS... I JUST--

"I'M JUST SOME GUY WHO MAKES MISSILES."

END

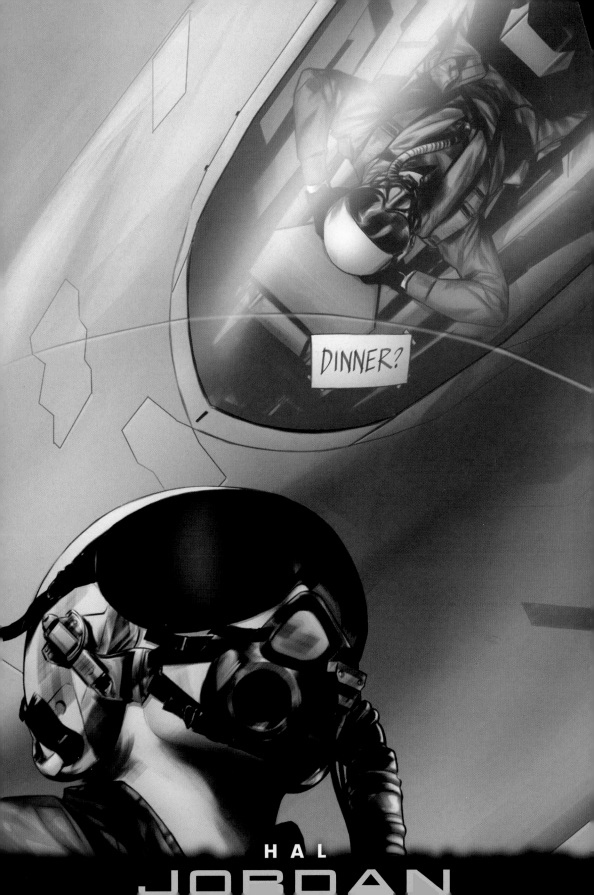

ADAM SCHLAGMAN
Writer

PART ONE: RISING TIDE
Art by **BEN OLIVER**
Cover by **RAGS MORALES** with **GABE ELTAEB**

PART TWO: BEWARE ITS POWER
Art by **CLIFF RICHARDS**
Cover by **FRANCIS PORTELA** with **JAVIER MEÑA**

PART THREE: HARD-TRAVELING HERO
Art by **CLIFF RICHARDS**
Cover by **J.G. JONES** with **ALEX SINCLAIR**

BOOOOMMM

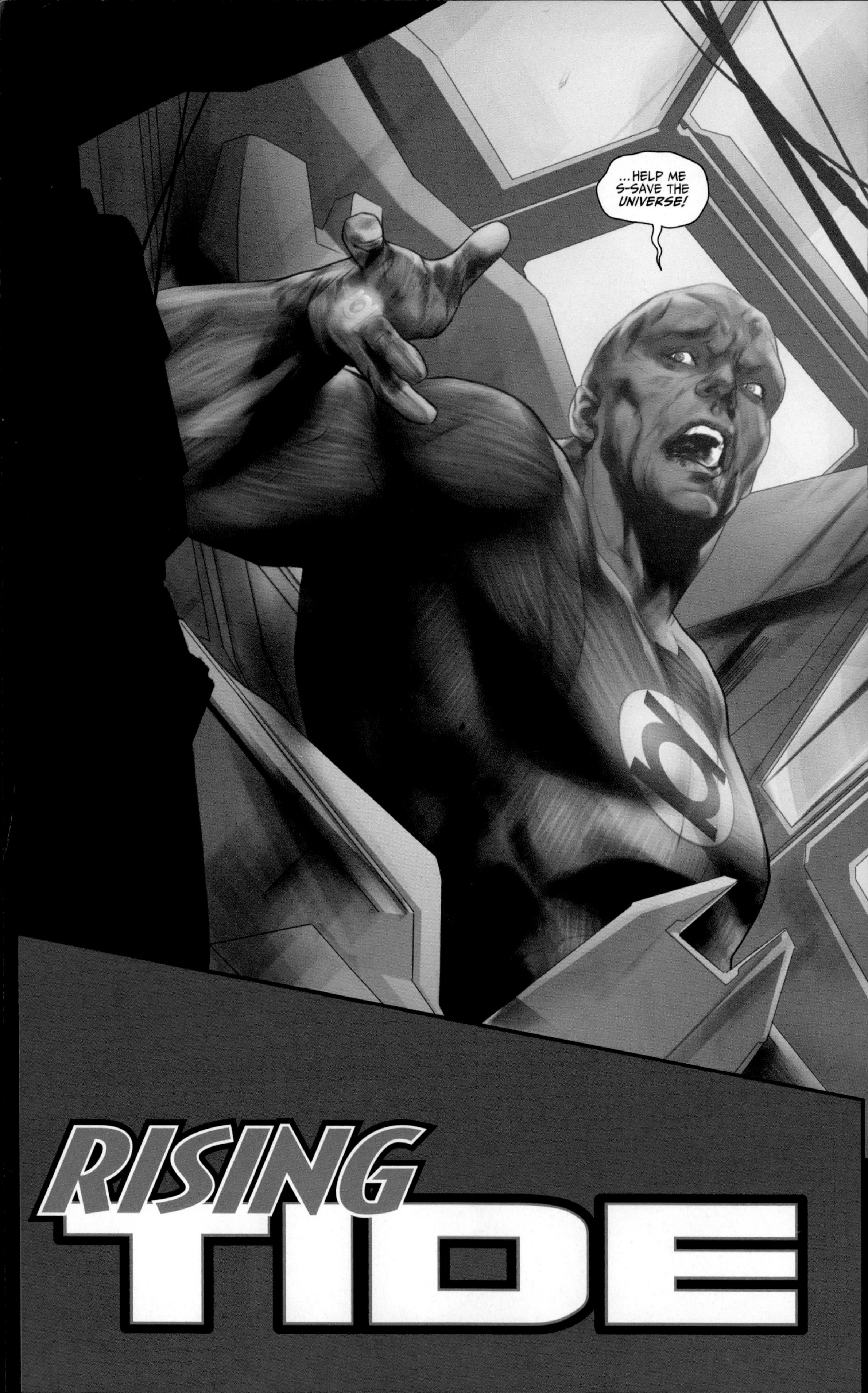
...HELP ME S-SAVE THE UNIVERSE!
RISING TIDE

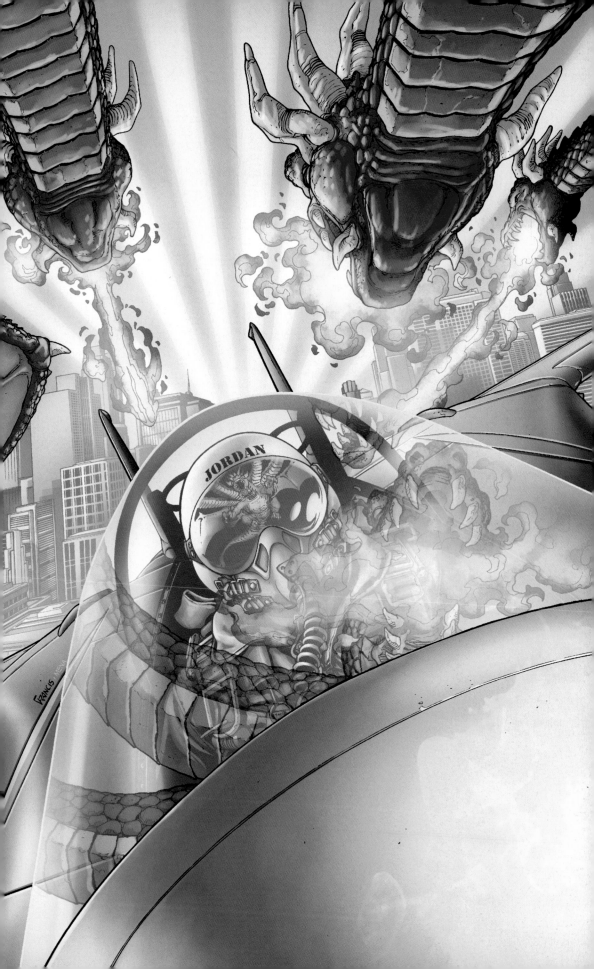

FIGURES THAT I'D GET STUCK WITH ONE.

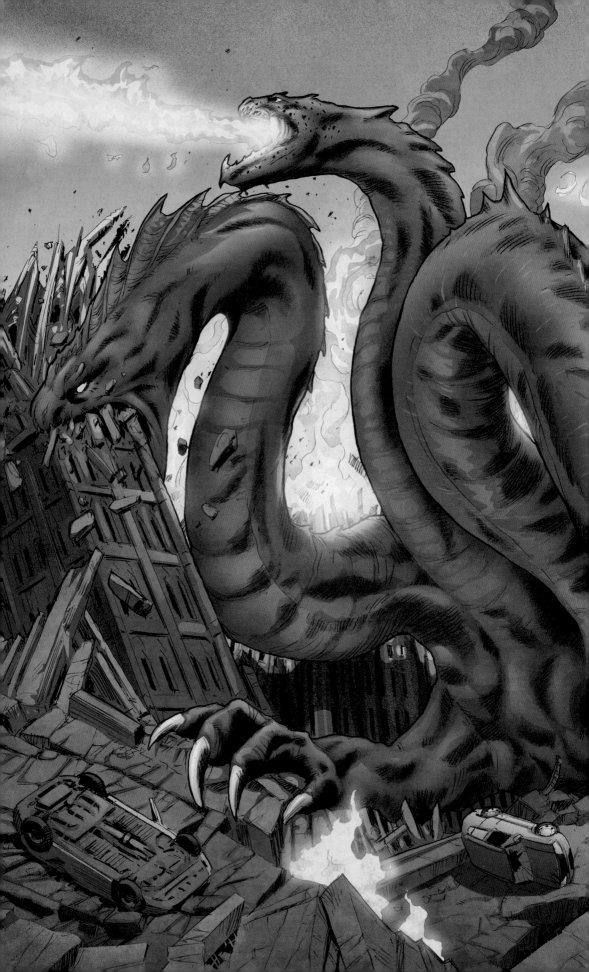

KROOOM!

"WE WON."

...WHEN IT'S UP TO ME TO SAVE IT.
BEWARE ITS POWER!
YOU'VE BEEN CHOSEN...
...TO DROP THE GREEN ARROW NUKE.
GOOD LUCK, PILOT.
THANK YOU, MISTER PRESIDENT.

GOODBYES ARE NEVER EASY.

NOKK NOKK

HEY, CAROL. LOOKING GREAT AS ALWAYS.

HAL, WHY'RE YOU HERE?

I JUST WANTED TO... UH--

TO WHAT, HAL?

I ALREADY TRIED TO TALK YOU OUT OF PILOTING THE NUKE TO ENGLAND--SO JUST WHAT'RE YOU TRYING TO SAY?

I-I CAME TO SAY... GOODBYE.

IT'S ALWAYS GOODBYE WITH YOU...

...BUT I'LL SAVE YOU THE TROUBLE OF SAYING IT YET AGAIN.

I'M COMING WITH YOU.

"SEE YOU ON THE TARMAC."

OPERATION: NIGHTLIGHT'S A GO!

KICK THE TIRES AND LIGHT THE FIRES, LET'S GET THESE BIRDS OFF THE GROUND. *MOVE MOVE MOVE!*

ECH. OF COURSE I'M ASSIGNED TO OUTFIT JORDAN'S PLANE, WHILE TOM GETS CAROL'S.

HOPE SHE'S READY TO *FLY*, HECTOR.

SHE IS, THANKS TO *ME*. IN LESS THAN TWENTY-FOUR HOURS, I MANAGED TO *REDESIGN* THE F-35, SHEDDING OVER *FOURTEEN HUNDRED POUNDS* AND THUS ENABLING IT TO CARRY THIS *OVERZEALOUS* STRIKE MISSILE.

THE *"GREEN ARROW."* THEY SAY IT *ALWAYS* HITS ITS TARGET.

GOD BLESS QUEEN INDUSTRIES.

AND *YOU*, HECTOR. YOU'RE A GENIUS.

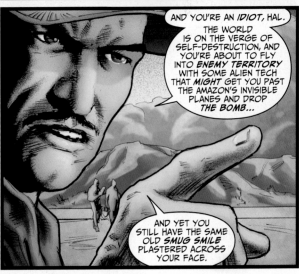

AND YOU'RE AN *IDIOT*, HAL. THE WORLD IS ON THE VERGE OF SELF-DESTRUCTION, AND YOU'RE ABOUT TO FLY INTO *ENEMY TERRITORY* WITH SOME ALIEN TECH THAT *MIGHT* GET YOU PAST THE AMAZON'S INVISIBLE PLANES AND DROP *THE BOMB...*

AND YET YOU STILL HAVE THE SAME OLD *SMUG SMILE* PLASTERED ACROSS YOUR FACE.

KA-THOOOM

KA-THOOOM

KA-THOOOM

DAMMIT! WE'VE GOT A *MAJOR* PROBLEM.

OPERATION: NIGHTLIGHT'S AT A STANDSTILL. THERE'S SOME KIND OF *INVISIBLE SHIELD* SURROUNDING THE ISLAND.

HIGHBALL, THINGS ARE ABOUT TO GET EVEN *WORSE*!

HARD-TRAVELING HERO
I LOVE YOU CAROL, AND ALWAYS HAVE.
I'VE JUST BEEN TOO AFRAID TO SAY
LOVE ALWAYS, YOUR HIGHBALL
Hal Jordan
END